A MATHEMATICAL

3-8
Years

WOULD YOU
RATHER
≫ GAME BOOK ≪

MATHSTICKS

A Mathematical
Would You Rather...
Game Book
for
6-8 Year Olds

"A Mathematical Would You Rather..." is a fun, problem solving game-book.

Players choose between two mathematical situations, once they've made a decision they can explore **why** they made that choice... and then prove it!

It's an amazing way to bringing maths into 'real life' in a quirky, fun way.

Also, asking a player to explain the reason for their decision boosts their understanding. The game also offers a fun way to share strategies, and it ensures everyone understands and practices important mathematical skills.

Ideal for children in Key Stage 1 (6-8 years). But anyone... yes, even adults, will enjoy talking about the mathematical choices too!

HOW TO USE THIS BOOK

If you are playing with another person, you each take it in turns to choose a question.

Every question begins with the words:
"Would You Rather..."
and then there are two choices.

- Read the question together.

- Then, both of you should make your own choice.

- Next, tell each other how you decided on **your** choice.

- Do you agree, or have you made different choices?

- It doesn't matter who is right or wrong - **the fun is in sharing ideas**.

- What calculations did you do?

- Can one of you convince the other that their answer is the best?

If you are playing alone, choose a question.

- Think about the choices, which one seems best to you?

- How do you know?

- What calculations did you do?

- How would you convince someone else that that is the best choice?

- Was it a tricky question or an easy one?

- Can you find another question that is similar?

- Make up your own **Mathematical Would You Rather** questions?

All of the questions can be answered by using mathematical skills and knowledge.

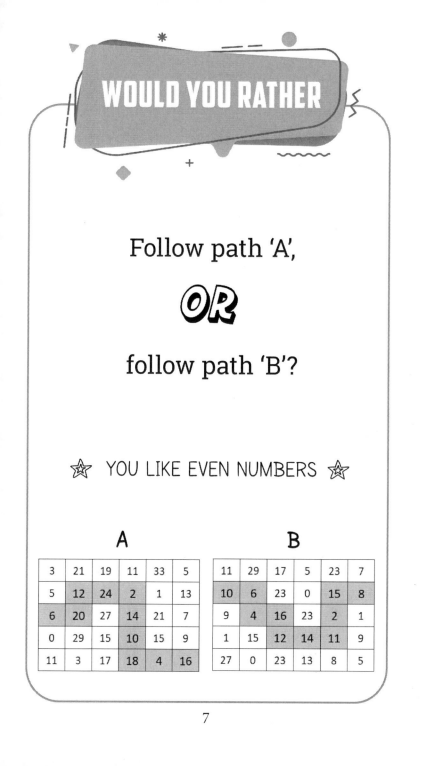

WOULD YOU RATHER

Follow path 'A',

OR

follow path 'B'?

⭐ YOU LIKE EVEN NUMBERS ⭐

A

3	21	19	11	33	5
5	12	24	2	1	13
6	20	27	14	21	7
0	29	15	10	15	9
11	3	17	18	4	16

B

11	29	17	5	23	7
10	6	23	0	15	8
9	4	16	23	2	1
1	15	12	14	11	9
27	0	23	13	8	5

Say, "the number of cubes here matches the page number,"

OR

"the number of cubes is less than the page number"?

Say, "the next number is odd,"

OR

"the next number is even"?

4, 11, 18, 25, 32, __

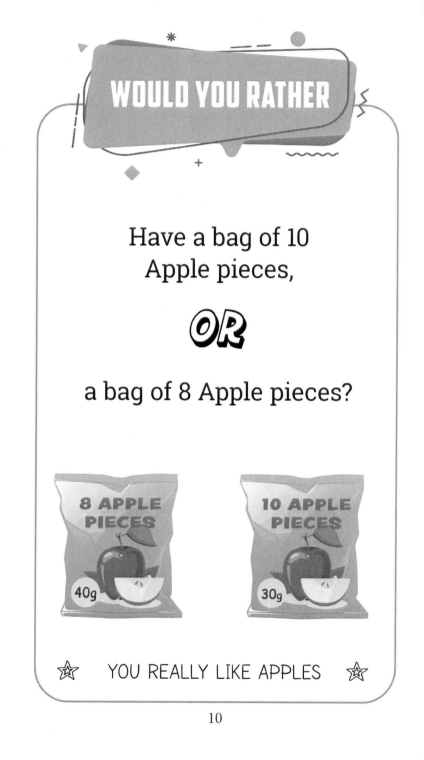

WOULD YOU RATHER

Have a bag of 10 Apple pieces,

OR

a bag of 8 Apple pieces?

YOU REALLY LIKE APPLES

WOULD YOU RATHER

Use

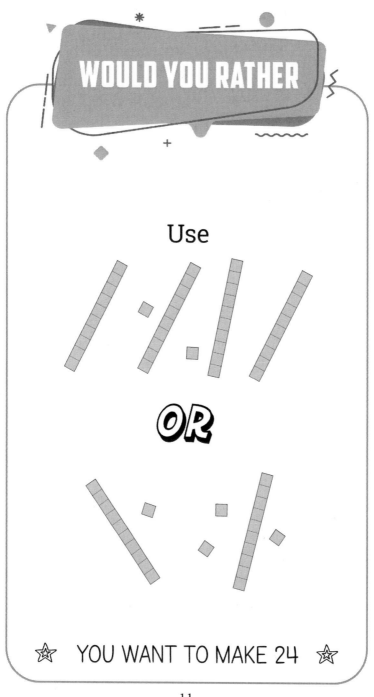

OR

YOU WANT TO MAKE 24

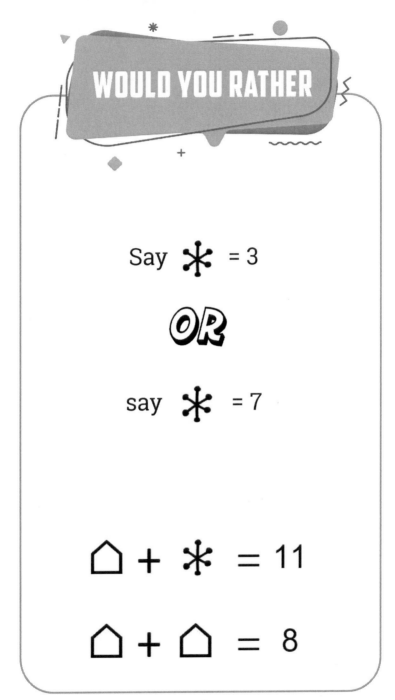

Say ✳ = 3

OR

say ✳ = 7

⌂ + ✳ = 11

⌂ + ⌂ = 8

Say, "Always!"

OR

"Sometimes!"

OR

"Never!"?

NUMBERS STARTING
WITH '2' ARE EVEN.

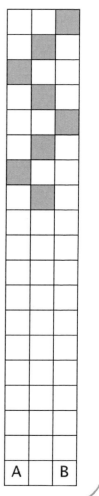

Finish the pattern on 'A',

finish the pattern on 'B'?

Say, "the hidden numbers are all even,"

OR

"some of the hidden numbers are even"?

Say, "there are more rectangles..."

OR

"there are more triangles"?

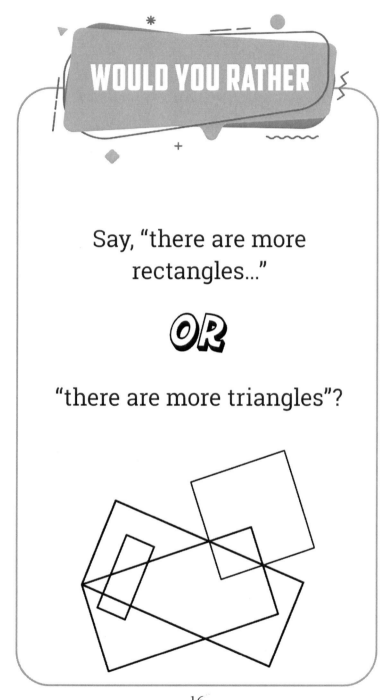

Show that this balance is correct,

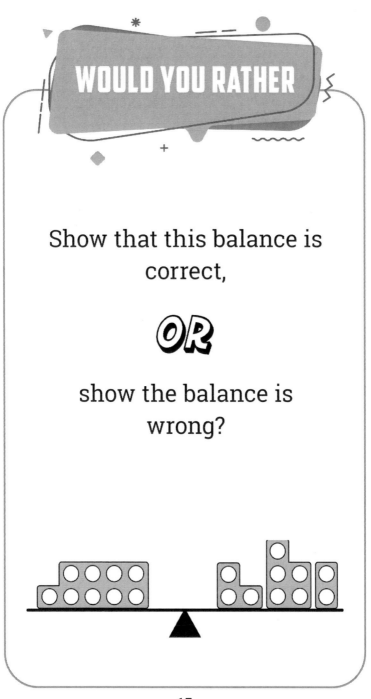

OR

show the balance is wrong?

Tell everyone the hidden shape could be a square,

OR

tell everyone it could be a triangle?

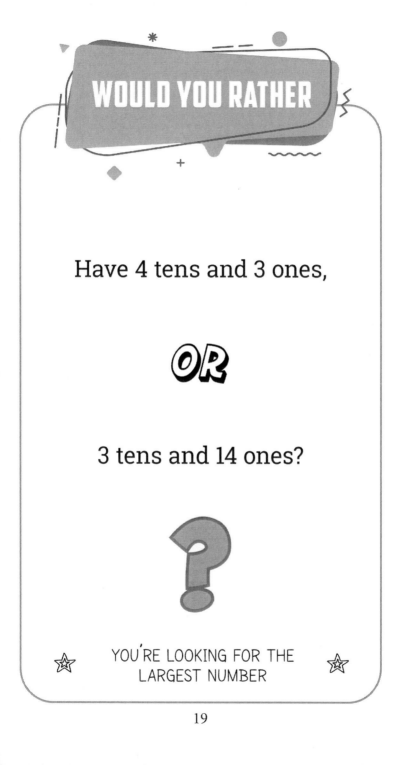

WOULD YOU RATHER

Have 4 tens and 3 ones,

OR

3 tens and 14 ones?

YOU'RE LOOKING FOR THE
LARGEST NUMBER

Say, "there are three hidden numbers,"

OR

"there are four hidden numbers"?

1 2 6 7 8

WOULD YOU RATHER

Have

🍎 🍦 �×ᐧ ✚ ∧

OR

🍎 👁 ♡ 👁 🗯

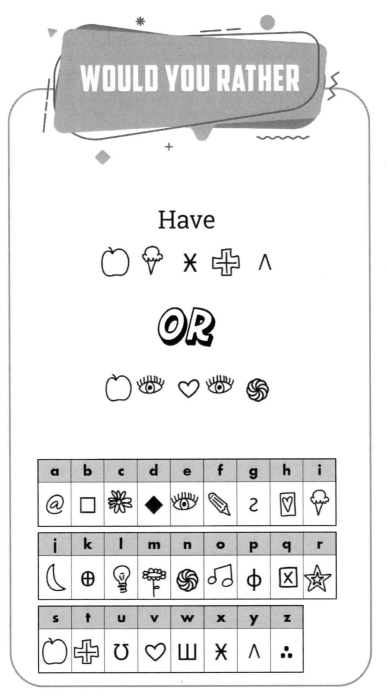

a	b	c	d	e	f	g	h	i
@	□	✿	◆	👁	✏	ᒣ	♡	🍦

j	k	l	m	n	o	p	q	r
🌙	⊕	💡	🌼	🌀	♫	φ	⊠	☆

s	t	u	v	w	x	y	z
🍎	✚	℧	♡	Ш	✗	∧	∴

Have the sum of all the numbers on the right,

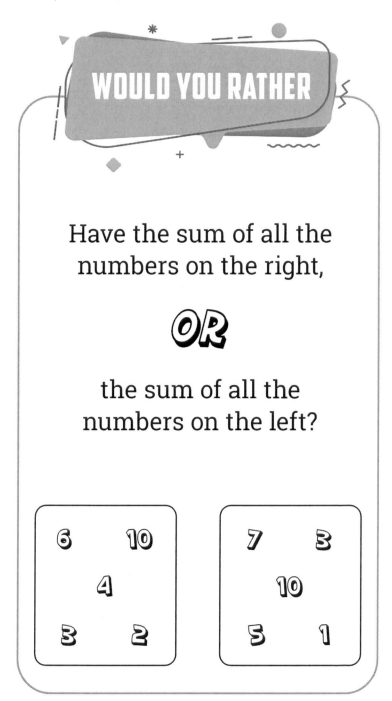

OR

the sum of all the numbers on the left?

6	10
	4
3	2

7	3
	10
5	1

WOULD YOU RATHER

Say, "the covered number is even,"

OR

"the number is odd"?

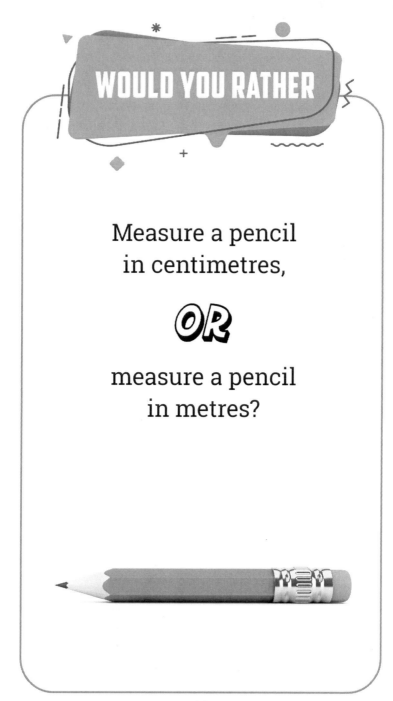

WOULD YOU RATHER

Measure a pencil
in centimetres,

OR

measure a pencil
in metres?

Use pattern 'A',

OR

pattern 'B'?

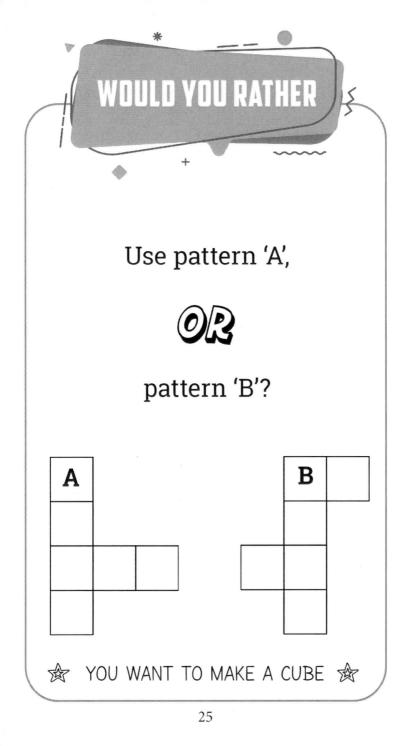

☆ YOU WANT TO MAKE A CUBE ☆

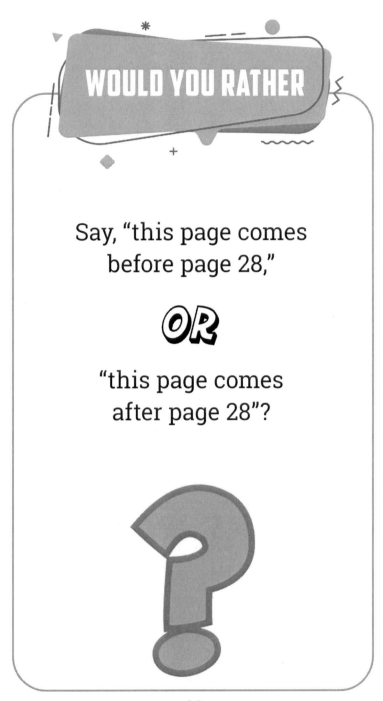

WOULD YOU RATHER

Say, "this page comes before page 28,"

OR

"this page comes after page 28"?

Have the sum of all the even numbers on a dice

OR

the sum of all the odd numbers?

⭐ YOU LIKE BIG NUMBERS ⭐

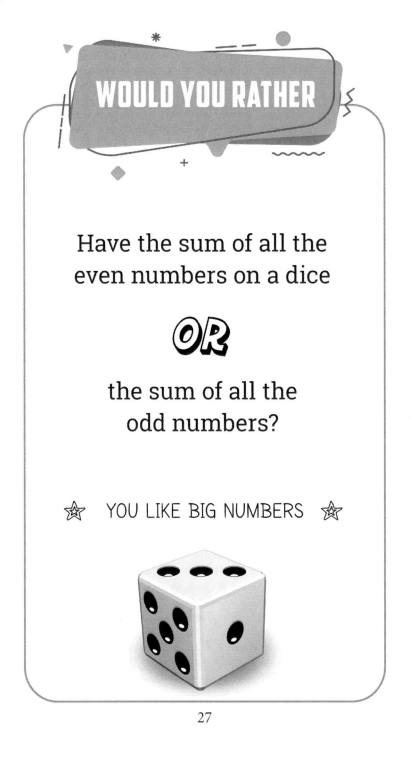

Agree with Bob,

OR

disagree with Bob?

THE NUMBERS ON THIS
CLOCK ARE WRONG

Say, "Always!"

OR

"Sometimes!"

OR

"Never!"?

"RECTANGLES ARE LONGER THAN SQUARES."

WOULD YOU RATHER

Have half of Paula's chocolate bar,

OR

half of Ed's chocolate bar?

Paula's chocolate

Ed's chocolate

Complete the pattern with

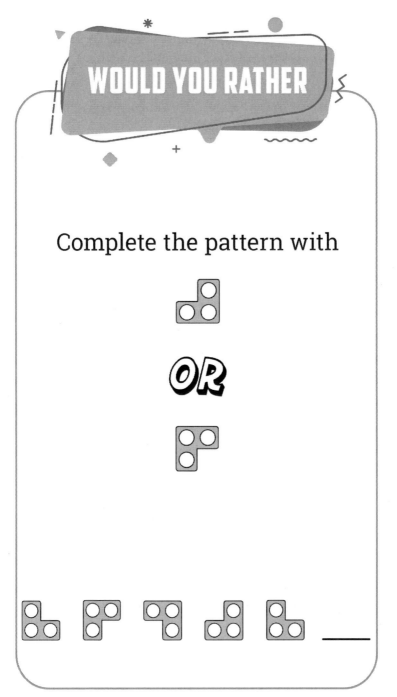

Say, "the largest number you can make with the two digits is even,"

OR

"the largest number is odd"?

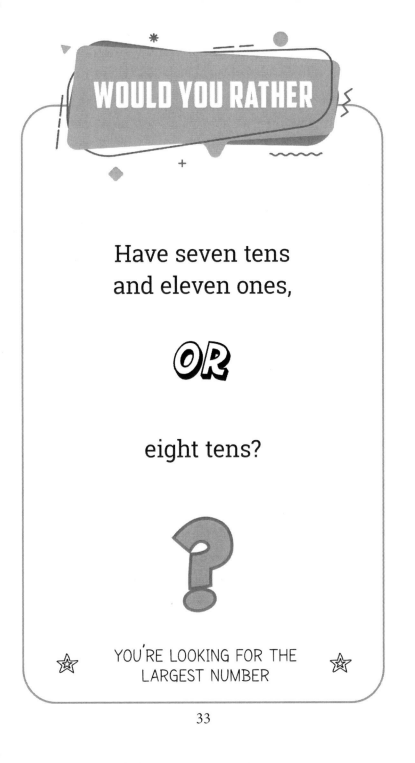

Have seven tens
and eleven ones,

OR

eight tens?

YOU'RE LOOKING FOR THE
LARGEST NUMBER

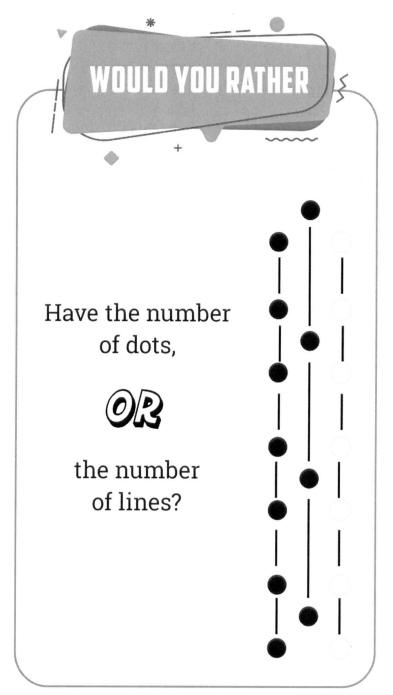

Have the number
of dots,

OR

the number
of lines?

Get 50p change,

OR

40p change?

YOU STARTED WITH £1
AND SPENT THESE COINS

Say "the clock
shows 4 o'clock,"

OR

"the clock shows
half-past 4"?

Tell everyone fourteen
is bigger than 39,

tell them forty is
bigger than 13?

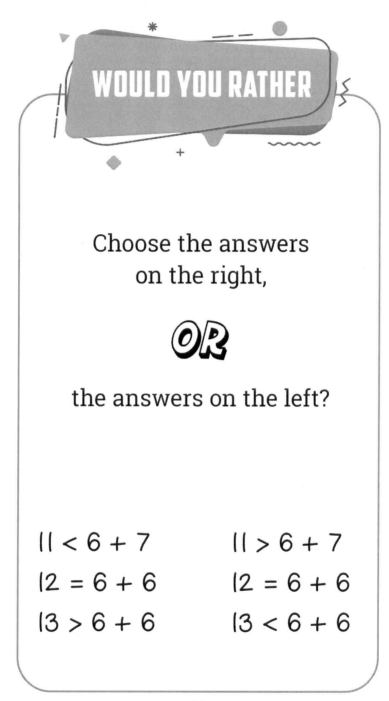

WOULD YOU RATHER

Choose the answers
on the right,

OR

the answers on the left?

11 < 6 + 7	11 > 6 + 7
12 = 6 + 6	12 = 6 + 6
13 > 6 + 6	13 < 6 + 6

Be like Jenny who got 8
house points but then
lost half of them,

like Sam who got 5
house points?

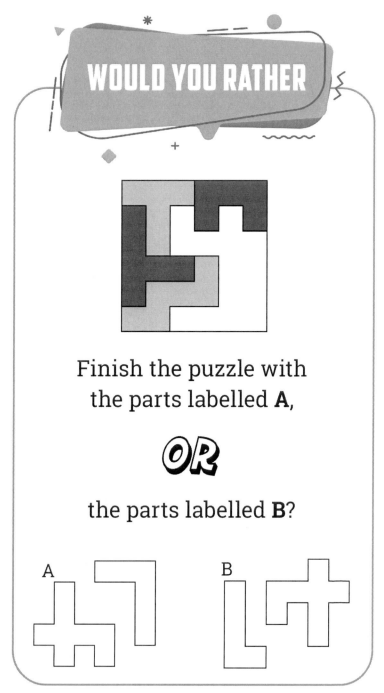

Finish the puzzle with
the parts labelled **A**,

OR

the parts labelled **B**?

A

B

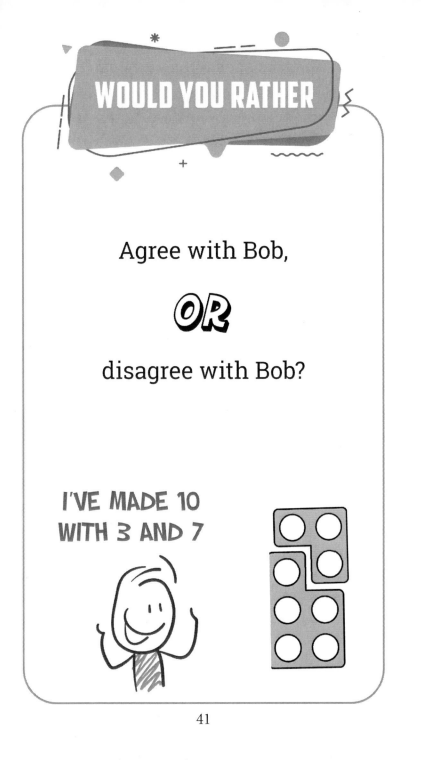

Agree with Bob,

OR

disagree with Bob?

I'VE MADE 10
WITH 3 AND 7

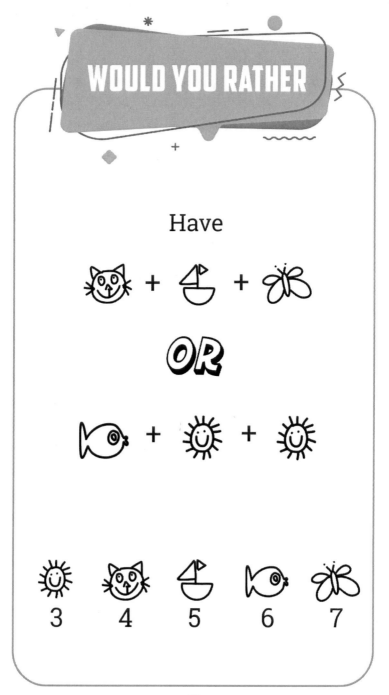

Have

🐱 + ⛵ + 🦋

OR

🐟 + ☀ + ☀

☀	🐱	⛵	🐟	🦋
3	4	5	6	7

Use

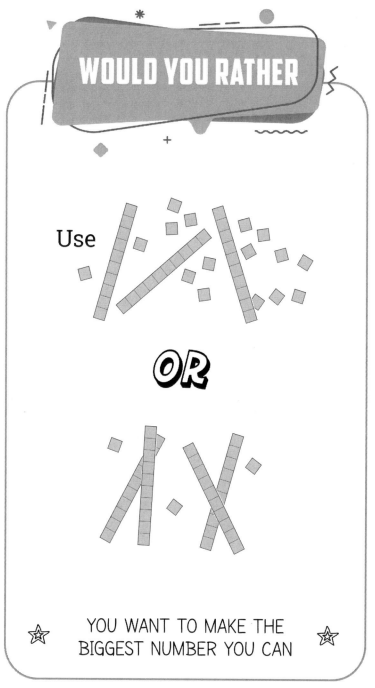

OR

YOU WANT TO MAKE THE
BIGGEST NUMBER YOU CAN

WOULD YOU RATHER

Say, "some letters are missing from this alphabet,"

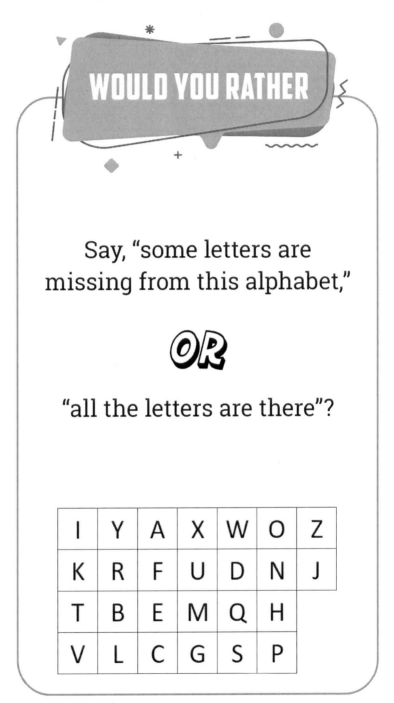

OR

"all the letters are there"?

I	Y	A	X	W	O	Z
K	R	F	U	D	N	J
T	B	E	M	Q	H	
V	L	C	G	S	P	

Find **two** diamonds
that don't belong,

OR

find **one** diamond that
doesn't belong?

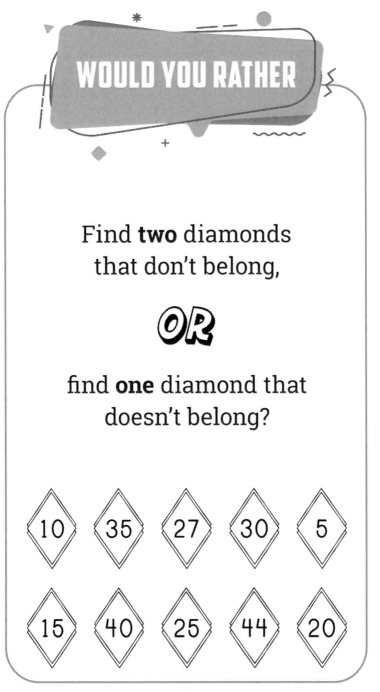

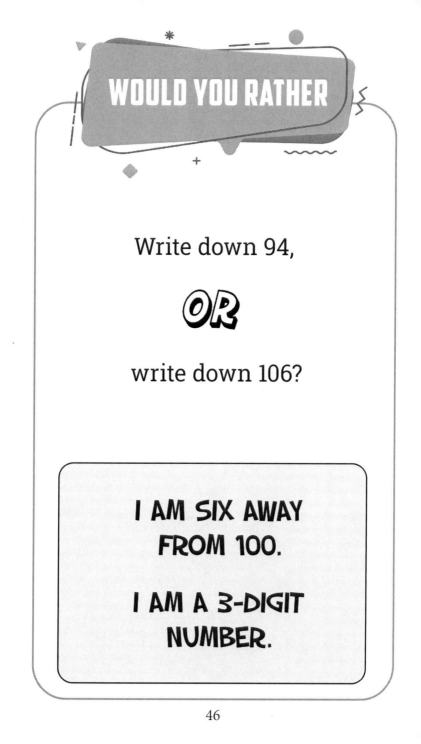

Write down 94,

OR

write down 106?

I AM SIX AWAY FROM 100.

I AM A 3-DIGIT NUMBER.

Say, "there are more dark cubes,"

OR

"there are more light cubes"?

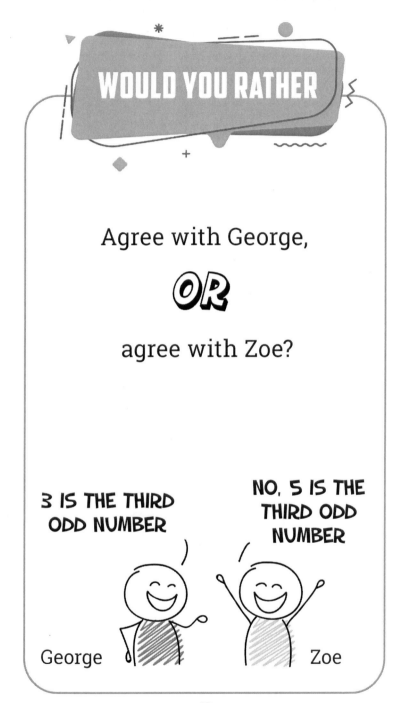

WOULD YOU RATHER

Agree with George,

OR

agree with Zoe?

3 IS THE THIRD ODD NUMBER

NO, 5 IS THE THIRD ODD NUMBER

George

Zoe

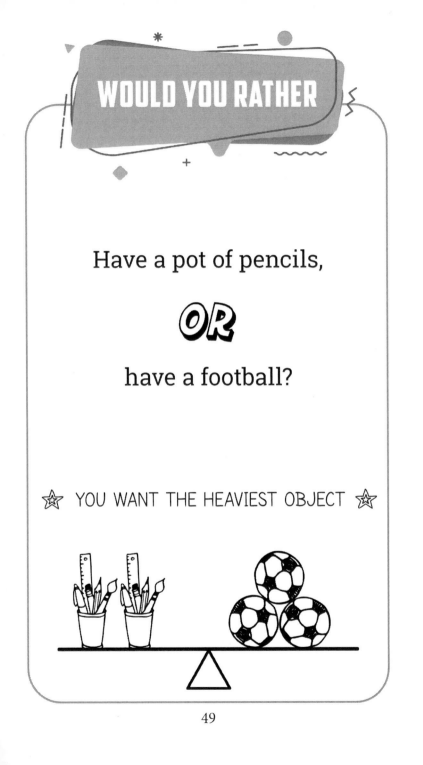

WOULD YOU RATHER

Have a pot of pencils,

OR

have a football?

⭐ YOU WANT THE HEAVIEST OBJECT ⭐

Tell people the last missing number must be 40,

OR

the last missing number must be 45?

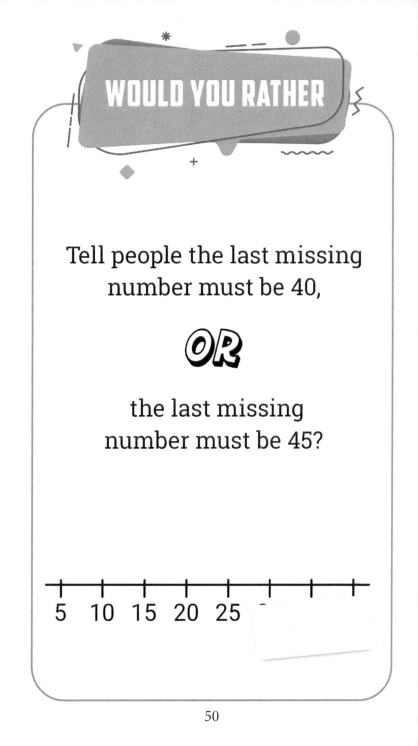

5   10   15   20   25

Say, "Always!"

OR

"Sometimes!"

OR

"Never!"?

ODD NUMBERS
ARE BIGGER THAN
EVEN NUMBERS.

Have the coins on the right,

OR

the coins on the left?

Say, "there are more triangles,"

OR

"there are more squares"?

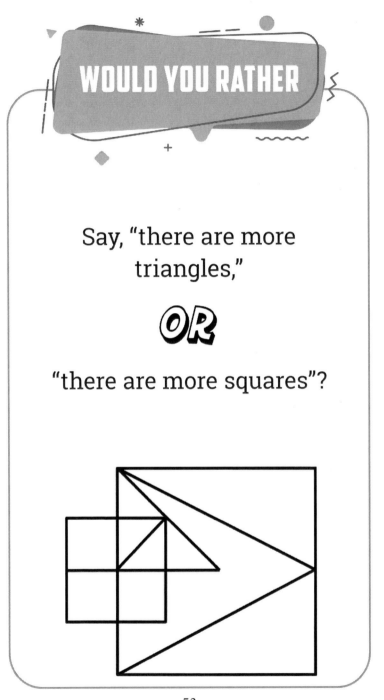

Agree with Ann,

OR

agree with Jack?

SOME MULTIPLES OF 5 ARE EVEN

MULTIPLES OF 5 ARE ALWAYS ODD

Ann

Jack

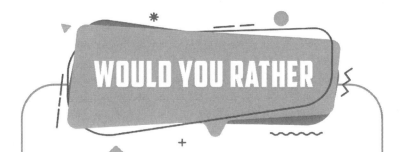

Have the sum of the first two numbers that start with the letter 'T'

the sum of the first two numbers that start with the letter 'F'?

WOULD YOU RATHER

Say, "it's just before 3 o'clock,"

OR

"it's just after 3 o'clock"?

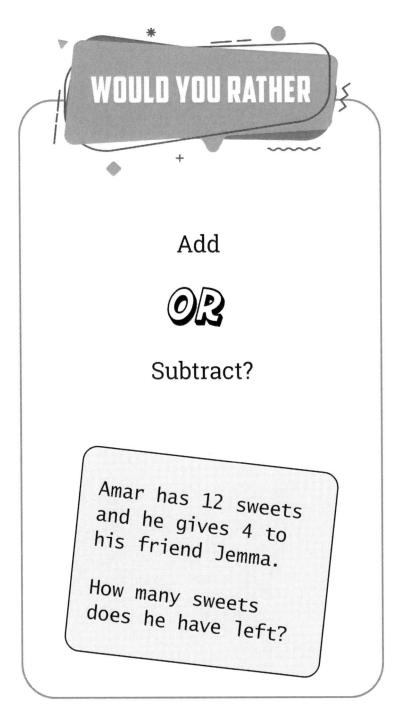

WOULD YOU RATHER

Add

OR

Subtract?

Amar has 12 sweets and he gives 4 to his friend Jemma.

How many sweets does he have left?

Use these three shapes
to make a triangle,

OR

use these three shapes
to make a square?

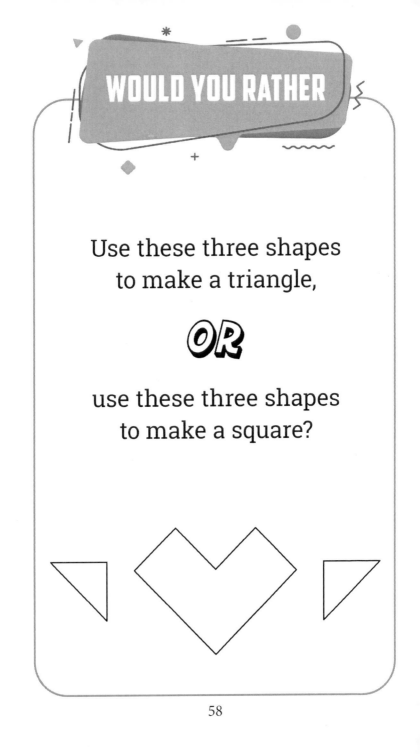

Say, "the missing number is 15,"

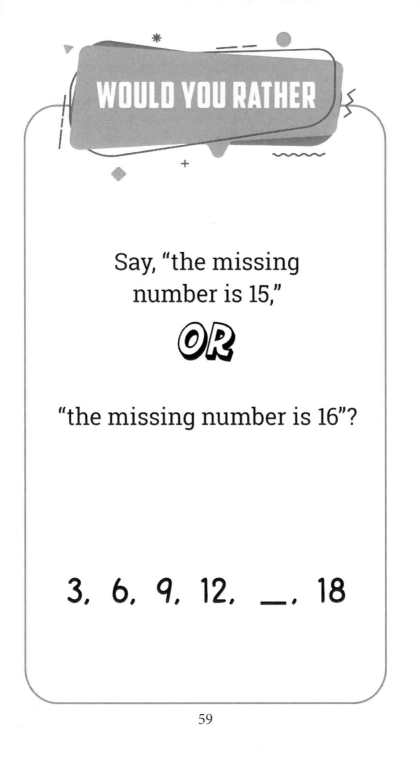

OR

"the missing number is 16"?

3, 6, 9, 12, __, 18

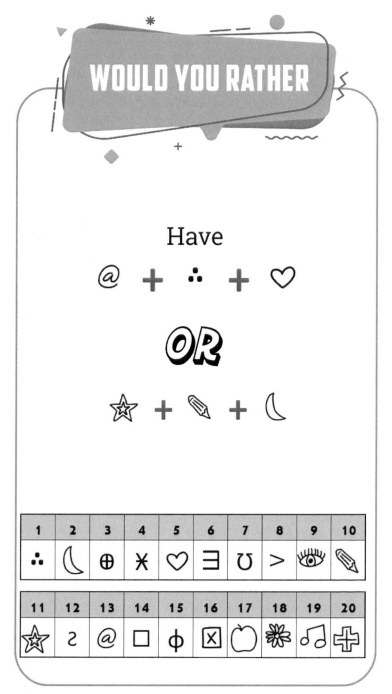

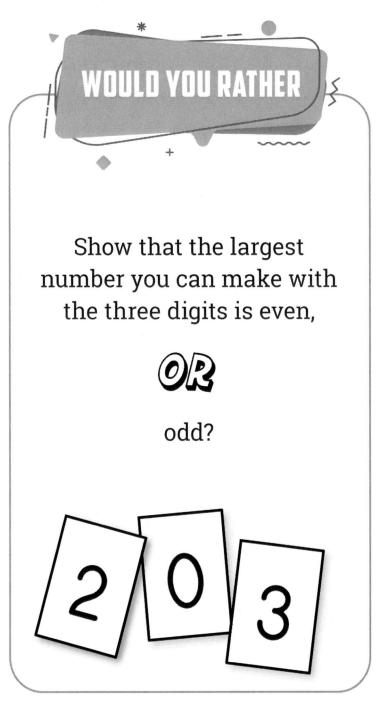

Show that the largest number you can make with the three digits is even,

OR

odd?

The difference
between 19 and 12

half the difference
between 15 and 3?

Finish the
pattern on 'A',

finish the
pattern on 'B'?

Make 54

OR

make 45?

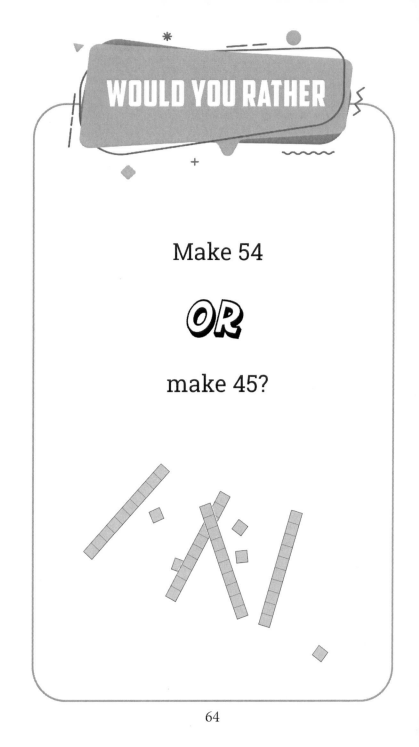

Say, "there are more triangles than squares,"

OR

"there are more squares than triangles"?

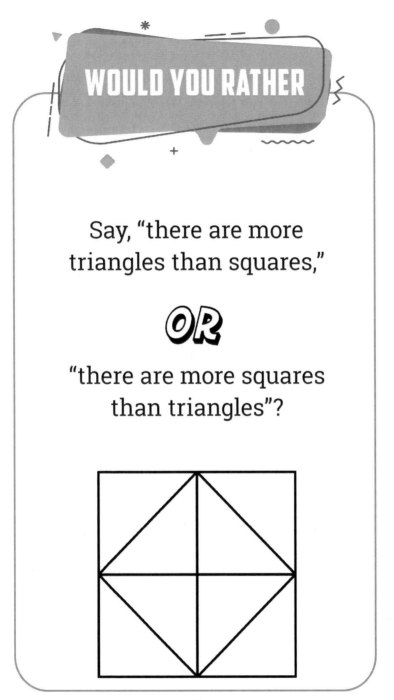

WOULD YOU RATHER

Tell your friend it's just before 9 o'clock,

OR

tell them it's just after 9 o'clock?

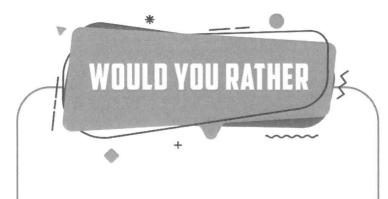

WOULD YOU RATHER

Prove that there is an
odd number of balls,

an even number of balls?

67

Roll a 4 and then a 5,

OR

roll a 5 and then a 4?

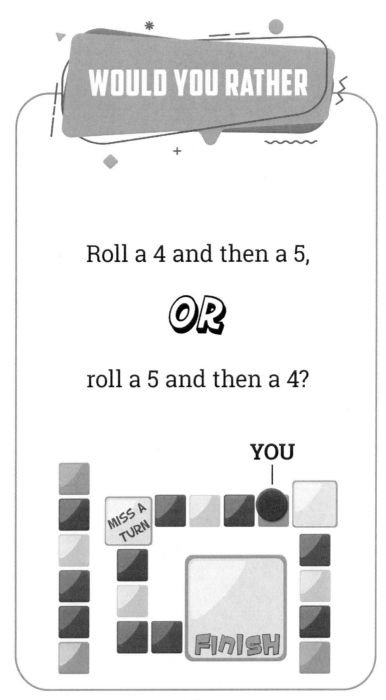

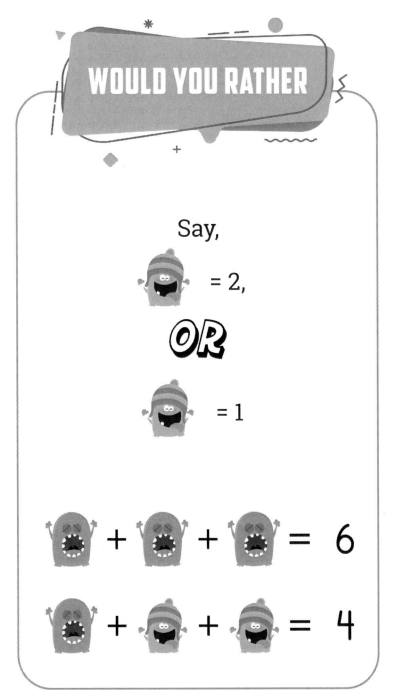

Say,

= 2,

OR

= 1

= 6

= 4

WOULD YOU RATHER

Agree with Bob,

OR

disagree with Bob?

FIVE 20 PENCE COINS ARE WORTH £1.00

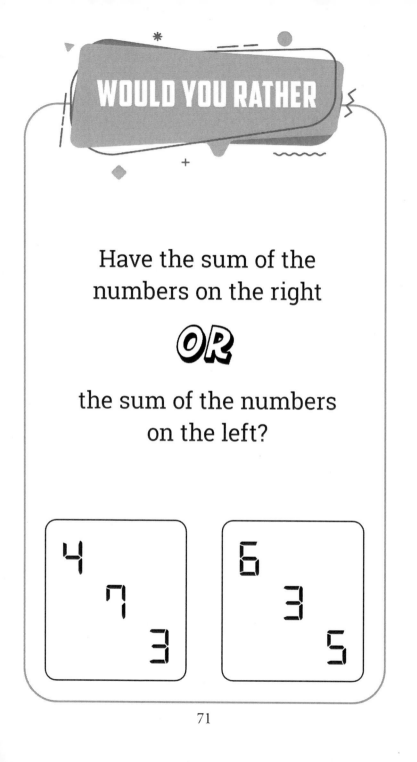

Use $>$

OR

$<$

$5 + 3 \boxed{?} 3 + 7$

Say, "Always!"

OR

"Sometimes!"

OR

"Never!"?

"CIRCLES ARE BIGGER THAN HALF CIRCLES!"

Tell your friends it's
half-past two,

OR

tell them it's
quarter-past six?

Say, "the box tips over and looks like **A**,"

OR

"the box tips over and looks like **B**"?

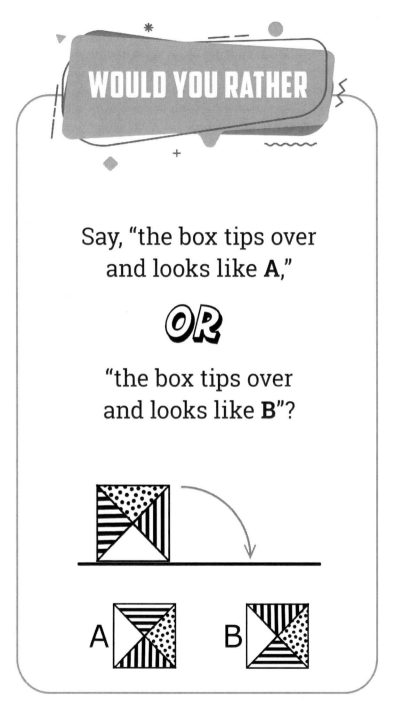

Agree with Bob,

OR

disagree with Bob?

DOUBLE 7
IS THE SAME
AS 6 + 8

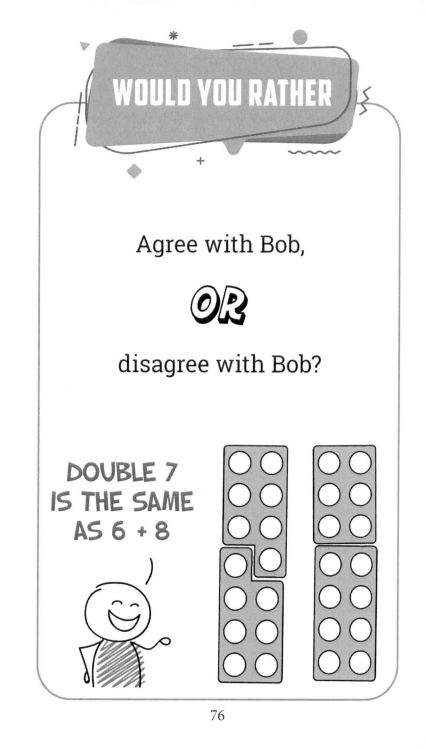

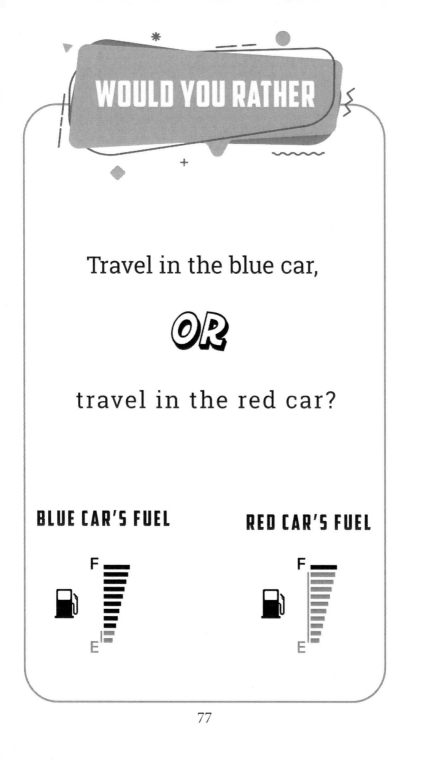

WOULD YOU RATHER

Travel in the blue car,

OR

travel in the red car?

BLUE CAR'S FUEL

RED CAR'S FUEL

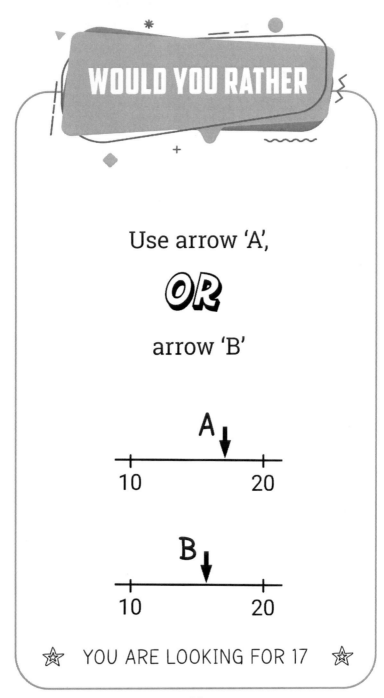

Use arrow 'A',

OR

arrow 'B'

A ↓

10 ——————————— 20

B ↓

10 ——————————— 20

☆ YOU ARE LOOKING FOR 17 ☆

Say, "half of 20 is the same as double 5,"

OR

"double 20 is smaller than 30"?

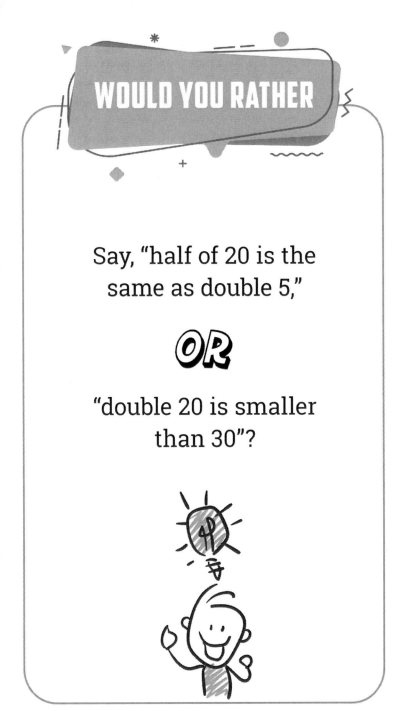

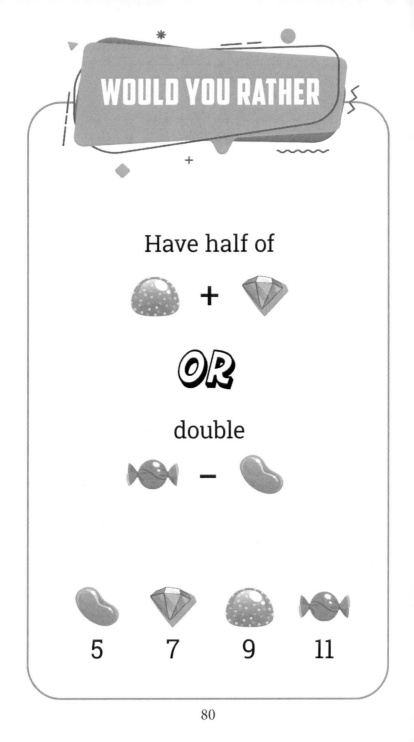

Have half of

🍬 **+** 💎

OR

double

🍬 **−** 🫘

5   7   9   11

WOULD YOU RATHER

Agree with Lucy,

OR

agree with Rob?

THE FOURTH SHAPE IS STRIPY

NO, THE FIFTH SHAPE IS STRIPY

Lucy

Rob

Get 41p change,

OR

39p change?

YOU STARTED WITH £1 AND
SPENT THESE COINS

Complete the pattern with

Say S + E + V + E + N is double 10,

OR

say E + V + E + N is odd?

A	B	C	D	E	F	G	H	I	J	K	L	M
1	2	3	4	5	1	2	3	4	5	1	2	3

N	O	P	Q	R	S	T	U	V	W	X	Y	Z
4	5	1	2	3	4	5	1	2	3	4	5	1

WOULD YOU RATHER

Use

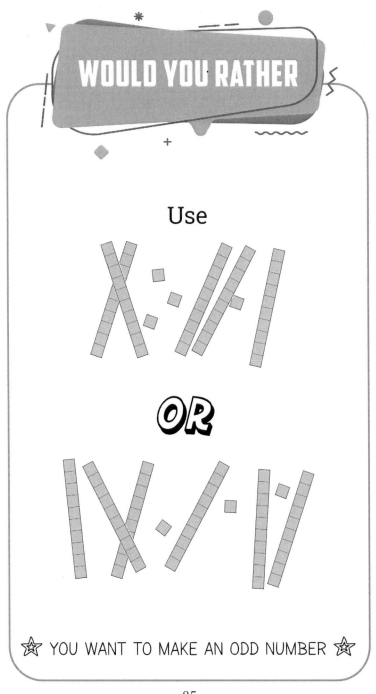

OR

☆ YOU WANT TO MAKE AN ODD NUMBER ☆

Say the missing numbers are "multiples of 10,"

OR

"multiples of 5"?

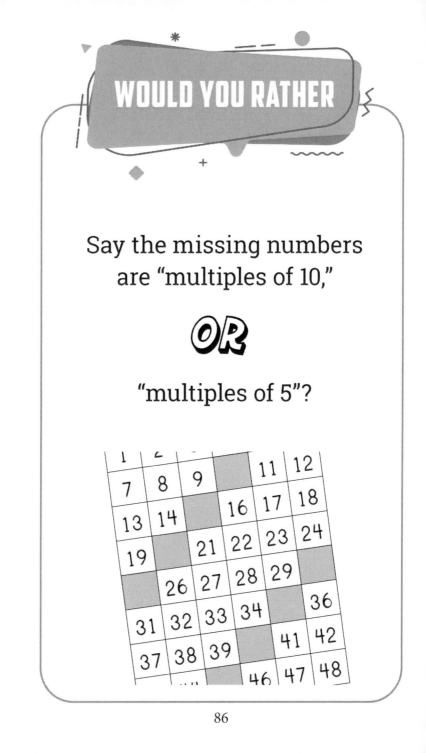

Say, "red is more popular than orange and green,"

"orange is more popular than blue, but not as popular as red"?

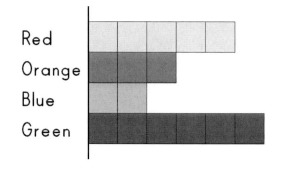

Have five lots of X,

OR

two lots of Y

$$X + X = 6$$
$$Y + X = 8$$

WOULD YOU RATHER

Agree with Alex,

OR

agree with Tia?

THERE ARE
12 MONTHS
IN A YEAR

THERE ARE
30 MONTHS
IN 3 YEARS

Alex

Tia

Use these shapes to make a square,

OR

use these shapes to make a triangle?

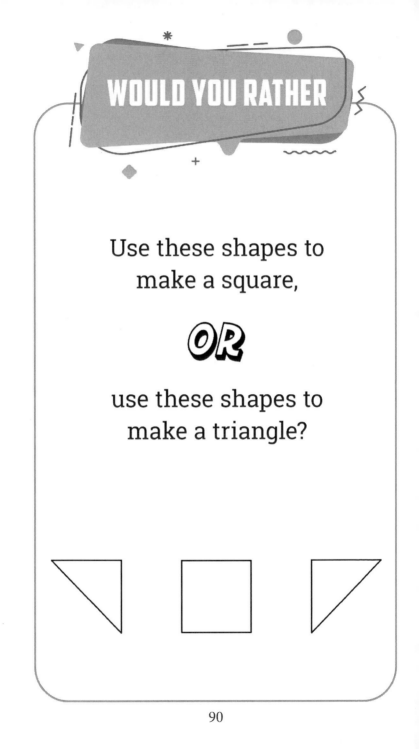

Say, this book is "heavier than 1 kilogram,"

OR

"lighter than 1 kilogram"?

WOULD YOU RATHER

Have

☆ + 🎁 + 🍓

OR

🦋 + ◇ + ☆

🎁	🦋	◇	🍓	☆
3	5	6	9	11

WOULD YOU RATHER

Have the sum of
4 and 5 and 6,

OR

have 'three lots of four'?

☆ YOU LIKE BIG NUMBERS ☆

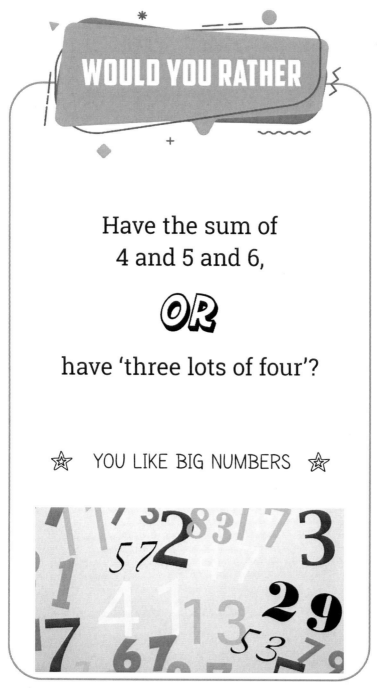

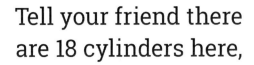

Tell your friend there are 18 cylinders here,

tell them there are 16 cylinders here?

Say, "I can make a number larger than five hundred,"

OR

"the largest number is less than five hundred"?

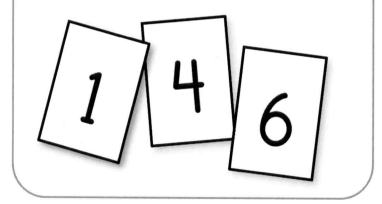

Say, "Always!"

OR

"Sometimes!"

OR

"Never!"?

"TRIANGLES ARE BIGGER THAN SQUARES."

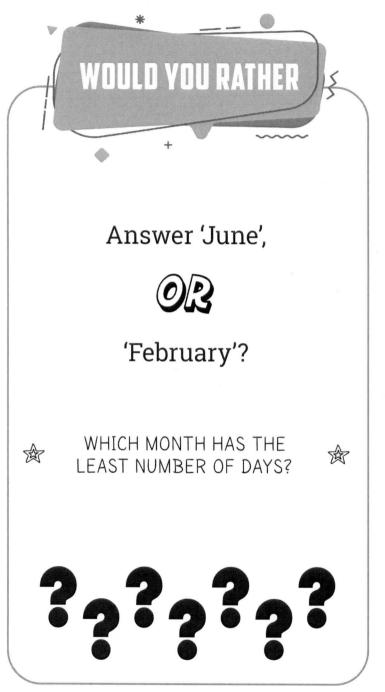

WOULD YOU RATHER

Answer 'June',

OR

'February'?

WHICH MONTH HAS THE
LEAST NUMBER OF DAYS?

Say, "it's just before half-past 4,"

OR

"it's just after half-past 4"?

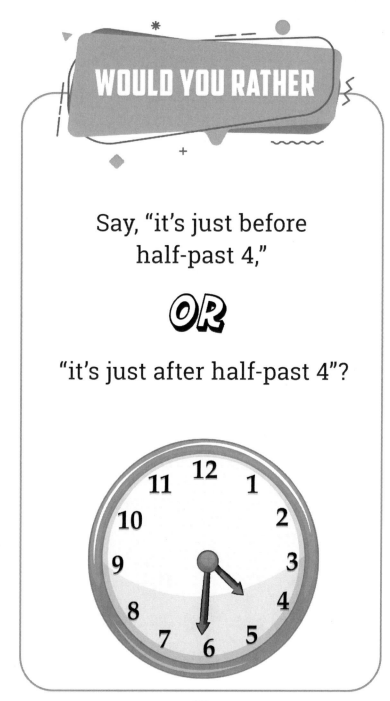

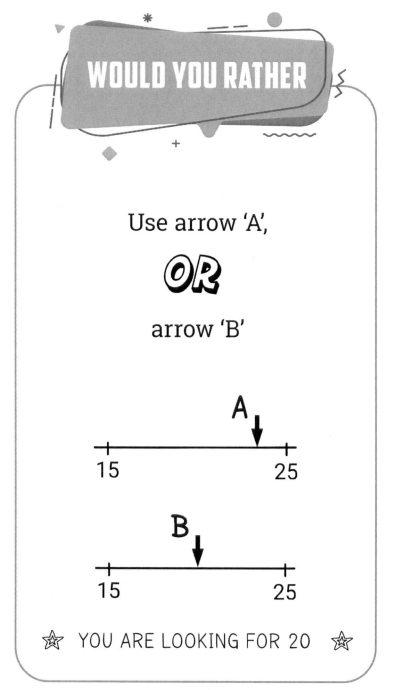

Use arrow 'A',

OR

arrow 'B'

A

```
+————————————————↓——+
15                 25
```

B

```
+————————↓——————————+
15                 25
```

☆ YOU ARE LOOKING FOR 20 ☆

Add

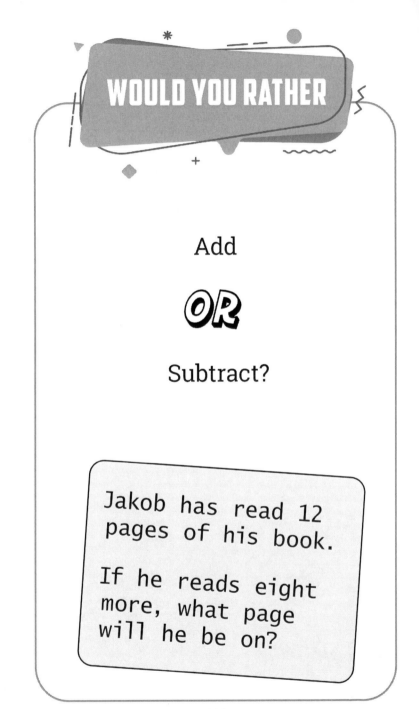

OR

Subtract?

Jakob has read 12 pages of his book.

If he reads eight more, what page will he be on?

Have 12 tens and 9 ones,

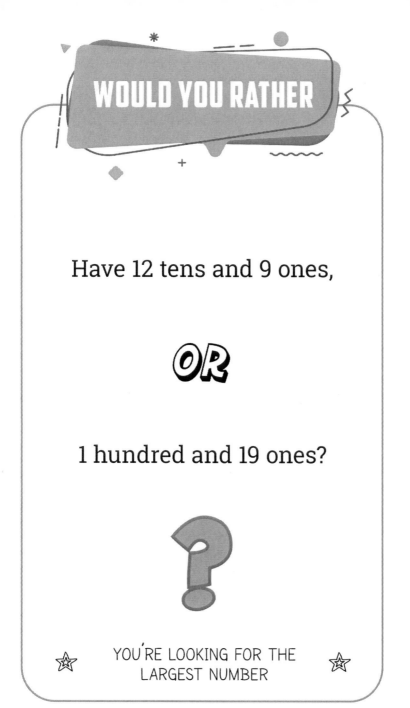

OR

1 hundred and 19 ones?

YOU'RE LOOKING FOR THE
LARGEST NUMBER

Tell your friend there are **three** symmetrical shapes here,

OR

tell them there are **two** symmetrical shapes here?

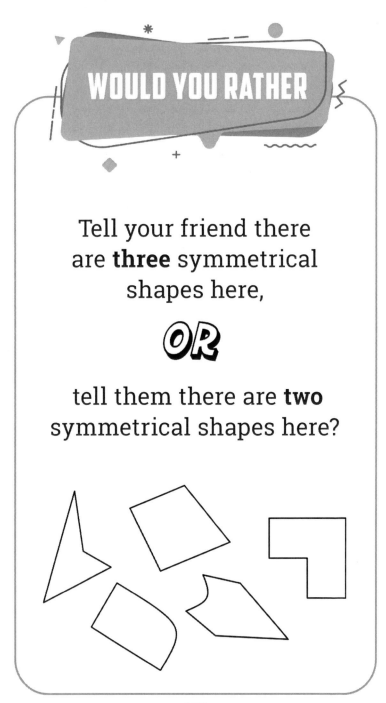

Say "the covered number is a multiple of 5,"

"the number isn't a multiple of 5"?

WOULD YOU RATHER

Argue that this
page number is the
same as 5 × 10,

OR

that this page number
is the same as 10 × 10?

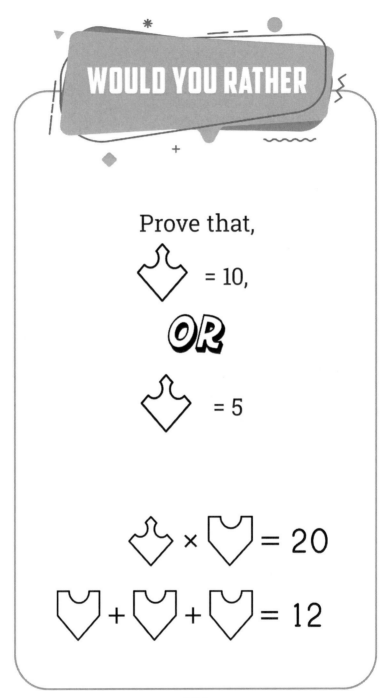

Prove that,

⬡ = 10,

OR

⬡ = 5

⬡ × ⬡ = 20

⬡ + ⬡ + ⬡ = 12

Have the number of sides
on three triangles,

OR

the number of sides
on two squares?

☆ YOU LIKE BIG NUMBERS ☆

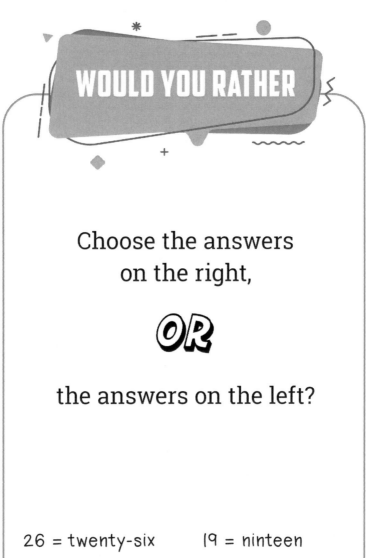

WOULD YOU RATHER

Choose the answers
on the right,

OR

the answers on the left?

26 = twenty-six   19 = ninteen

39 = thirty-nine   24 = twenty-four

41 = fourteen   35 = thirty-five

55 = fifty-five   48 = forty-eight

Say, "there are **two** hexagons",

OR

"there are **three** hexagons in this picture"?

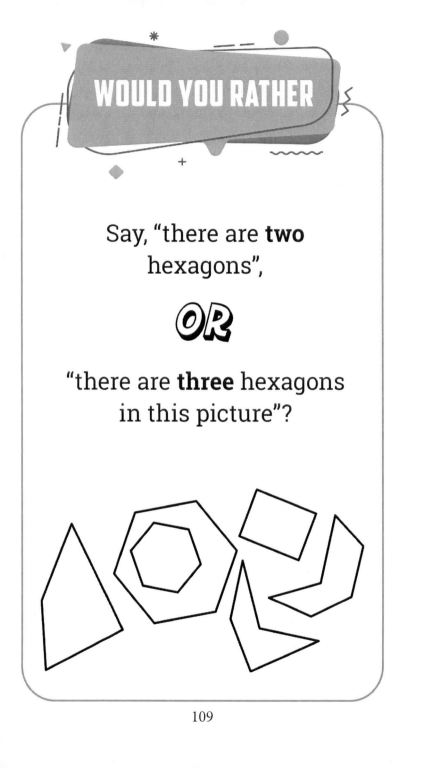

109

Have 'A',

OR

have 'B'?

A two add ten add thirteen

B three add nine add thirty

☆ YOU LIKE BIG NUMBERS ☆

Say, the tally shows "five more Magpies than Wrens have been to the bird feeder,"

"six more Robins than Wrens have been to the feeder"?

Wren	卌 l
Robin	卌 卌 ll
Magpie	卌 卌
Blackbird	卌 llll

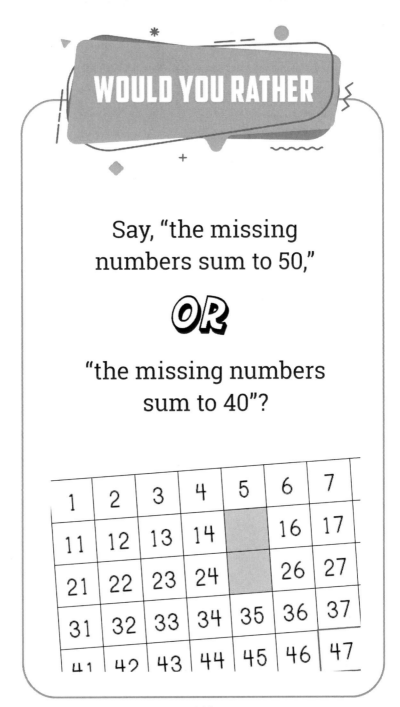

WOULD YOU RATHER

Say, "the missing numbers sum to 50,"

OR

"the missing numbers sum to 40"?

1	2	3	4	5	6	7
11	12	13	14		16	17
21	22	23	24		26	27
31	32	33	34	35	36	37
41	42	43	44	45	46	47

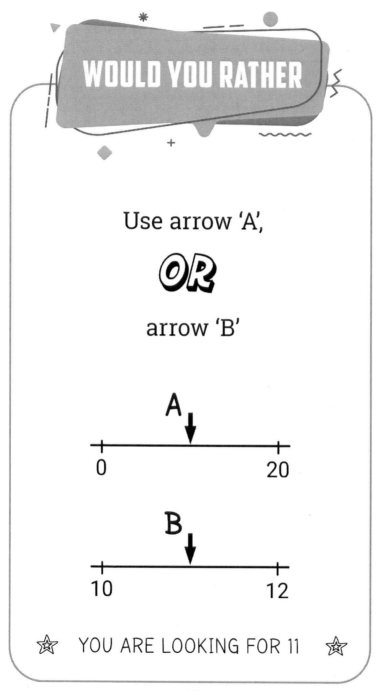

WOULD YOU RATHER

Use arrow 'A',

OR

arrow 'B'

A

0   20

B

10   12

☆ YOU ARE LOOKING FOR 11 ☆

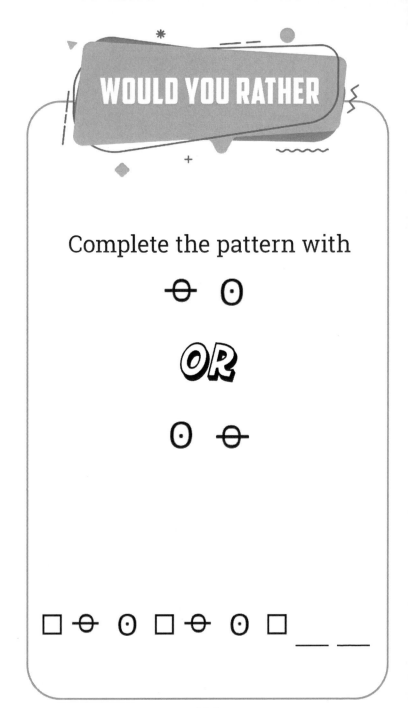

WOULD YOU RATHER

Complete the pattern with

⊖ ⊙

OR

⊙ ⊖

□ ⊖ ⊙ □ ⊖ ⊙ □ __ __

Say, T + W + E + L + V + E
is bigger than
T + H + I + R + T + E + E + N,

OR

T + H + I + R + T + E + E + N
is bigger than
T + W + E + L + V + E ?

A	B	C	D	E	F	G	H	I	J	K	L	M
1	2	3	4	5	1	2	3	4	5	1	2	3

N	O	P	Q	R	S	T	U	V	W	X	Y	Z
4	5	1	2	3	4	5	1	2	3	4	5	1

WOULD YOU RATHER

Agree with Olivia,

OR

agree with Drew?

THERE ARE 60 MINUTES IN AN HOUR

THERE ARE 100 MINUTES IN AN HOUR

Olivia

Drew

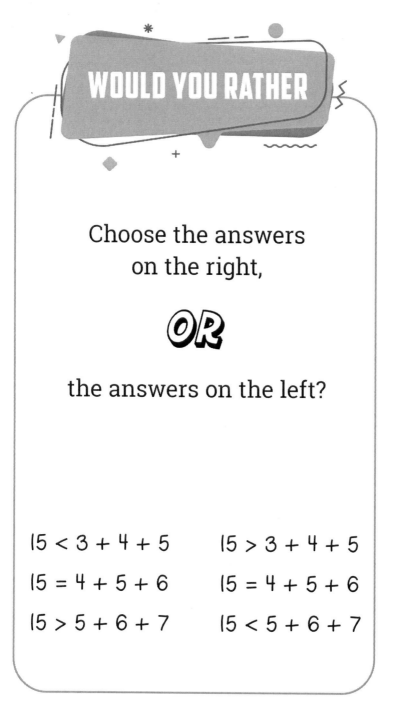

WOULD YOU RATHER

Choose the answers
on the right,

OR

the answers on the left?

15 < 3 + 4 + 5	15 > 3 + 4 + 5
15 = 4 + 5 + 6	15 = 4 + 5 + 6
15 > 5 + 6 + 7	15 < 5 + 6 + 7

Say, "it's a quarter-past 9,"

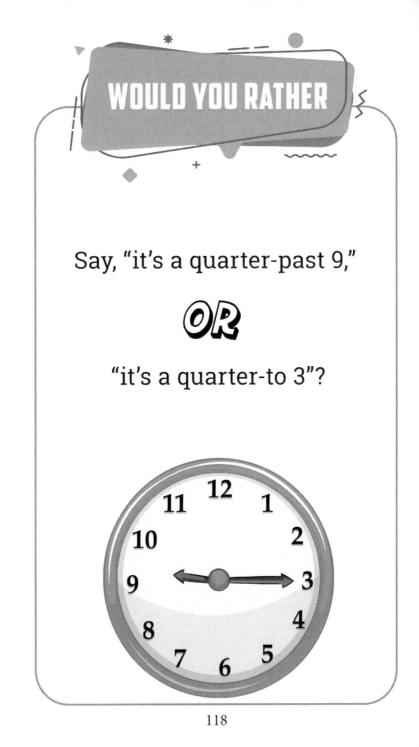

OR

"it's a quarter-to 3"?

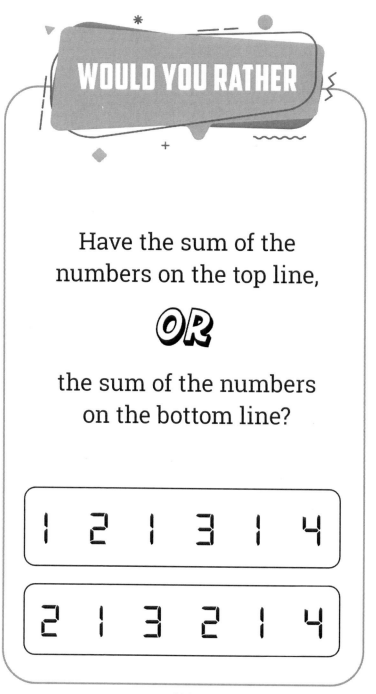

WOULD YOU RATHER

Have the sum of the numbers on the top line,

OR

the sum of the numbers on the bottom line?

1 2 1 3 1 4

2 1 3 2 1 4

Agree with Bob,

OR

disagree with Bob?

THERE ARE MORE CIRCLES
THAN ANY OTHER SHAPES HERE

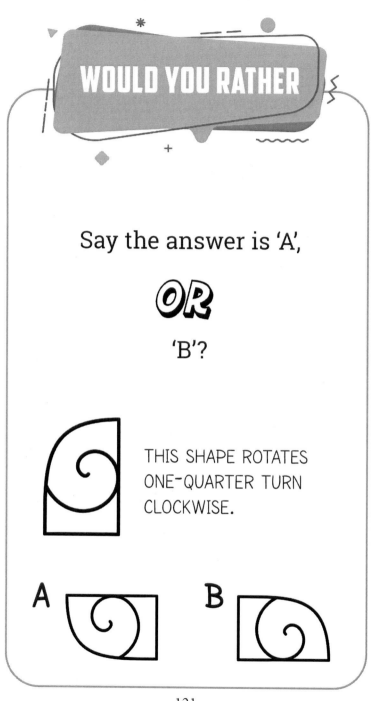

WOULD YOU RATHER

Say the answer is 'A',

OR

'B'?

THIS SHAPE ROTATES ONE-QUARTER TURN CLOCKWISE.

A

B

Follow route 'A',

OR

follow route 'B'?

A

5	18	0	32	28	40	21
4	16	31	8	7	20	9
3	12	24	10	23	36	18
17	38	1	19	29	15	42

B

8	4	0	17	18	10	14
13	20	32	28	26	0	1
14	30	26	40	17	16	12
0	22	21	24	36	44	11

☆ YOU LIKE MULTIPLES OF FOUR ☆

Say, "Always!"

OR

"Sometimes!"

OR

"Never!"?

"PYRAMIDS HAVE MORE FACES THAN CUBES."

Say, "all of these squares are the same,"

OR

"one of these squares is different"?

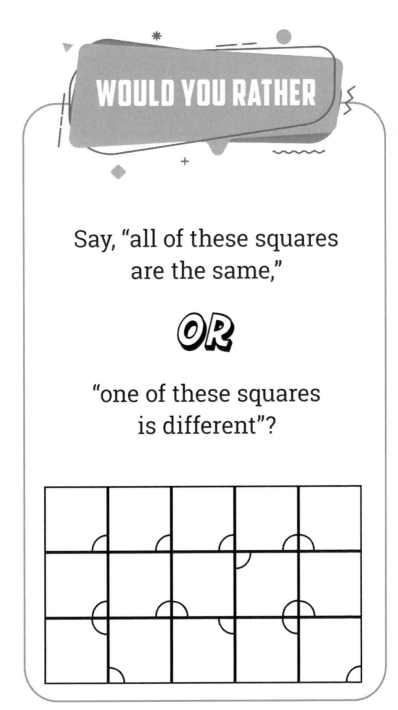

WOULD YOU RATHER

Have pizza every
Friday in August

OR

every Monday in August?

YOU REALLY LIKE PIZZA

AUGUST

S	M	T	W	T	F	S
						1
2	3	4	5	6	7	8
9	10	11	12	13	14	15
16	17	18	19	20	21	22
23	24	25	26	27	28	29
30	31					

Have

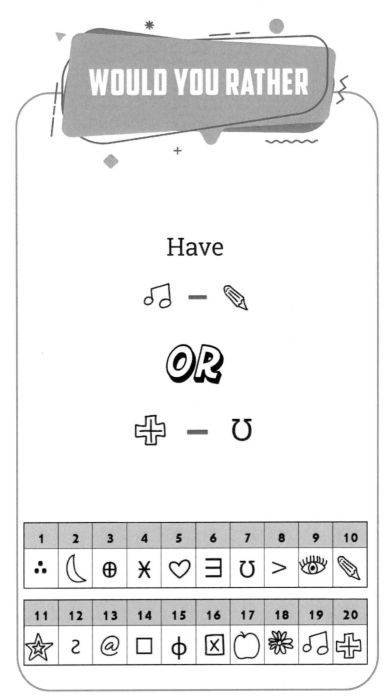

OR

1	2	3	4	5	6	7	8	9	10
∴	☾	⊕	✳	♡	∃	℧	>	👁	✎

11	12	13	14	15	16	17	18	19	20
☆	ς	@	□	φ	⊠	🍎	❋	♫	✚

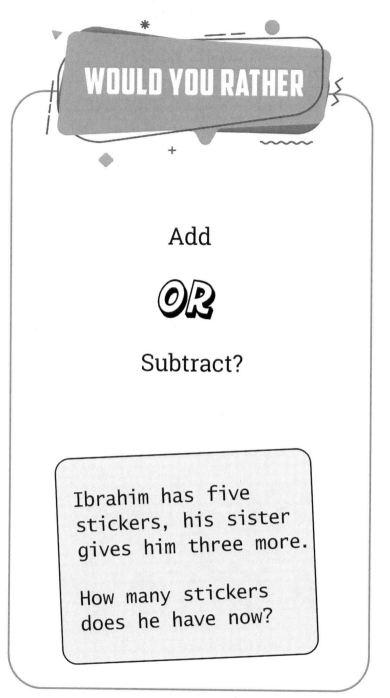

WOULD YOU RATHER

Add

OR

Subtract?

Ibrahim has five stickers, his sister gives him three more.

How many stickers does he have now?

Use

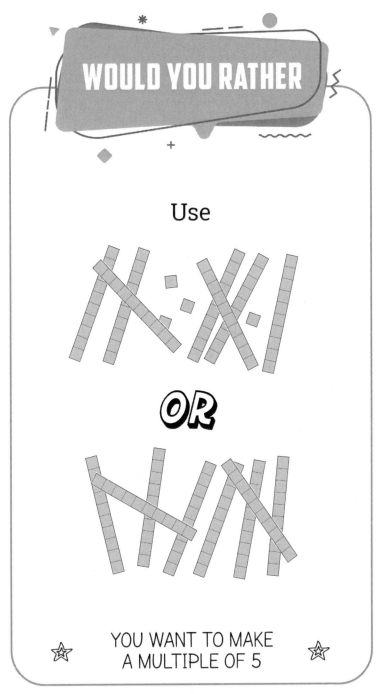

OR

YOU WANT TO MAKE
A MULTIPLE OF 5

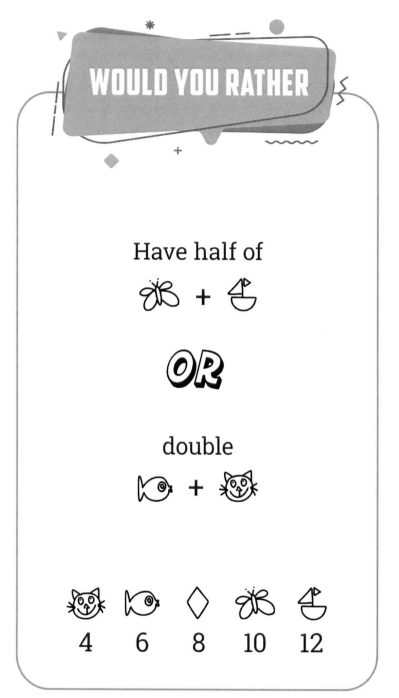

Have half of

🦋 + ⛵

OR

double

🐟 + 🐱

🐱	🐟	◇	🦋	⛵
4	6	8	10	12

Use pattern 'A',

OR

pattern 'B'?

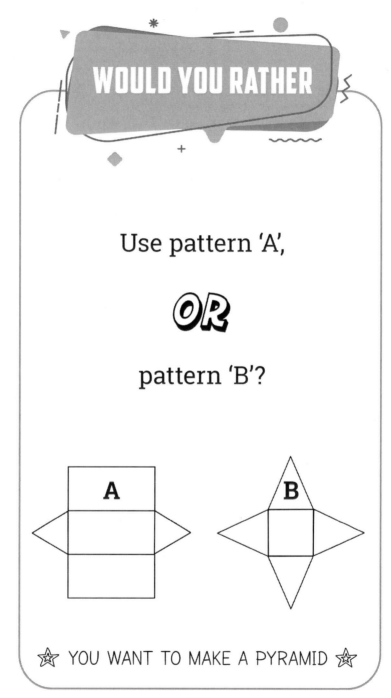

☆ YOU WANT TO MAKE A PYRAMID ☆

Use $>$

OR

$<$

OR

$=$

5 x 4   ?   10 x 2

Have the value of
C + O + A + T

OR

the value of
H + O + O + D

A	B	C	D	E	F	G	H	I	J	K	L	M
1	2	3	4	5	6	7	8	9	10	11	12	13

N	O	P	Q	R	S	T	U	V	W	X	Y	Z
14	15	16	17	18	19	20	21	22	23	24	25	26

Prove that the largest number you can make with the three digits is even

the largest number is odd?

Say, "it's a quarter-to three,"

OR

"it is a quarter-past nine"?

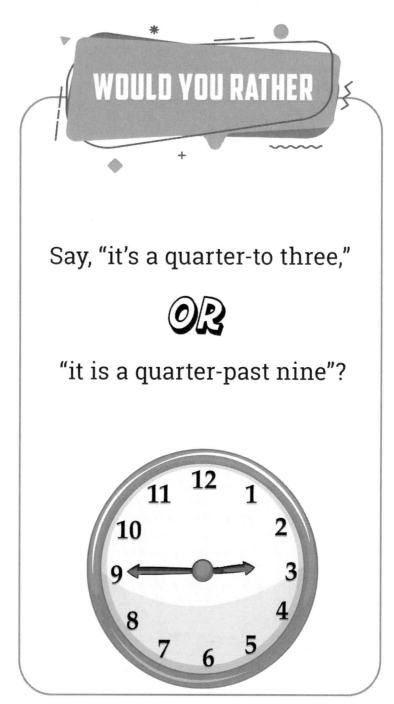

Say, "five more people liked cheese than jam,"

OR

"four more people liked jam than ham"?

Marmite	O O O O O O O O O
Jam	O O O O O O O O O O
Ham	O O O O O O
Cheese	O O O O O O O O O O O

Have **S M A L L ,**

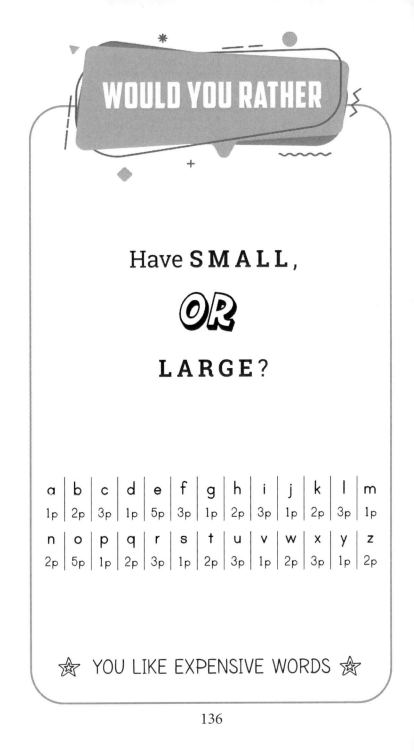

O R

L A R G E ?

a	b	c	d	e	f	g	h	i	j	k	l	m
1p	2p	3p	1p	5p	3p	1p	2p	3p	1p	2p	3p	1p

n	o	p	q	r	s	t	u	v	w	x	y	z
2p	5p	1p	2p	3p	1p	2p	3p	1p	2p	3p	1p	2p

⭐ YOU LIKE EXPENSIVE WORDS ⭐

Finish the
pattern on 'A',

finish the
pattern on 'B'?

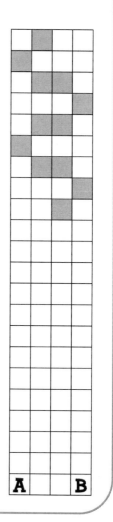

Say,

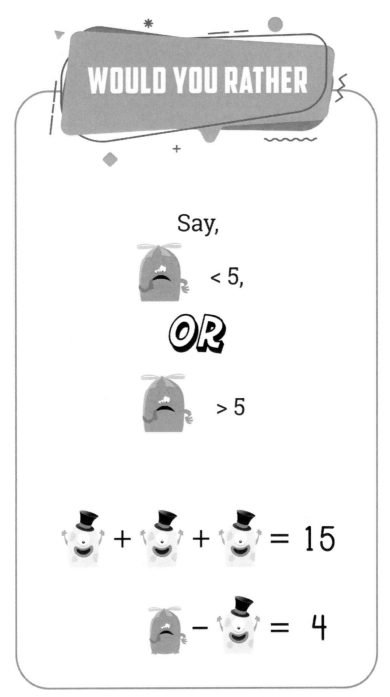

$$\text{(monster)} < 5,$$

OR

$$\text{(monster)} > 5$$

$$\text{(snowman)} + \text{(snowman)} + \text{(snowman)} = 15$$

$$\text{(monster)} - \text{(snowman)} = 4$$

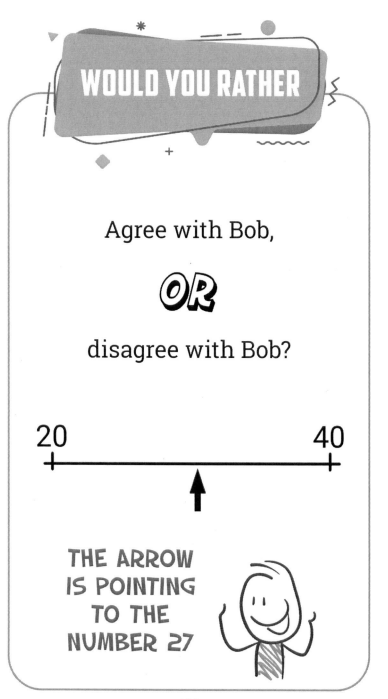

Agree with Bob,

OR

disagree with Bob?

20   40

THE ARROW IS POINTING TO THE NUMBER 27

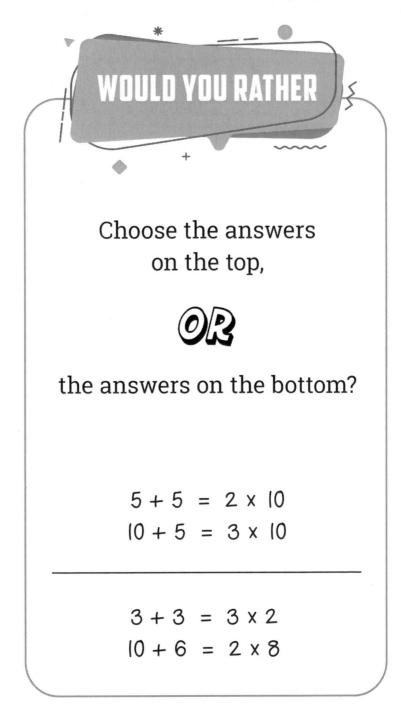

WOULD YOU RATHER

Choose the answers
on the top,

OR

the answers on the bottom?

$$5 + 5 = 2 \times 10$$
$$10 + 5 = 3 \times 10$$

$$3 + 3 = 3 \times 2$$
$$10 + 6 = 2 \times 8$$

Say, the missing
number in the middle
is "ten less than 16,"

"ten more than 16"?

42	43	44	45		47	48	49	5(
32	33	34	35		37	38	39	4(
12	13	14	15		17	18	19	20
2	3	4	5		7	8	9	10

Have double half of six,

OR

have half of double eight?

☆ YOU LIKE BIG NUMBERS ☆

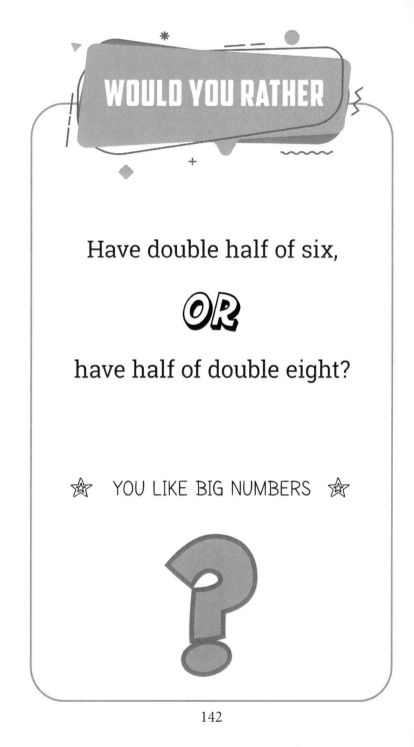

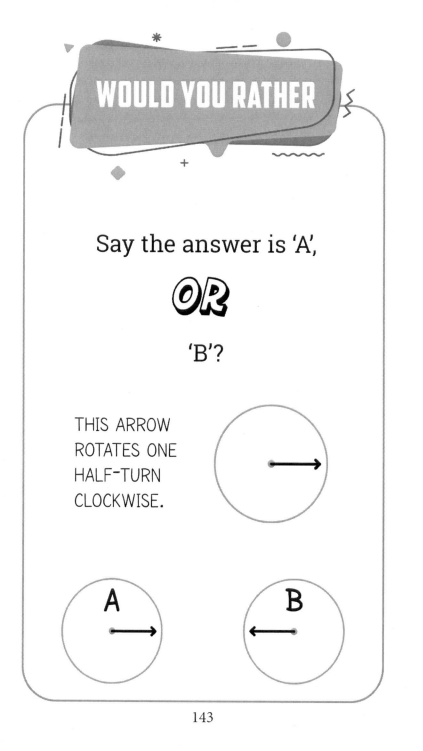

WOULD YOU RATHER

Say the answer is 'A',

OR

'B'?

THIS ARROW
ROTATES ONE
HALF-TURN
CLOCKWISE.

A

B

Say, "Always!"

OR

"Sometimes!"

OR

"Never!"?

NUMBERS IN THE
2X TABLE ARE IN
THE 5X TABLE.

WOULD YOU RATHER

Say, "the largest number you can make is bigger than two hundred,"

OR

"the largest number is bigger than four hundred"?

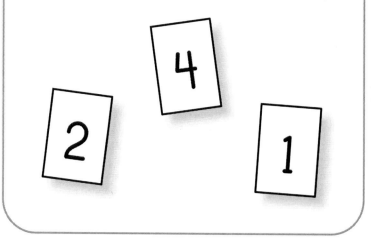

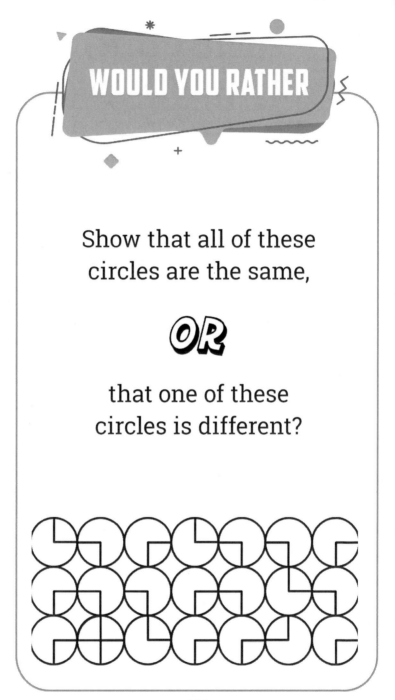

WOULD YOU RATHER

Show that all of these
circles are the same,

OR

that one of these
circles is different?

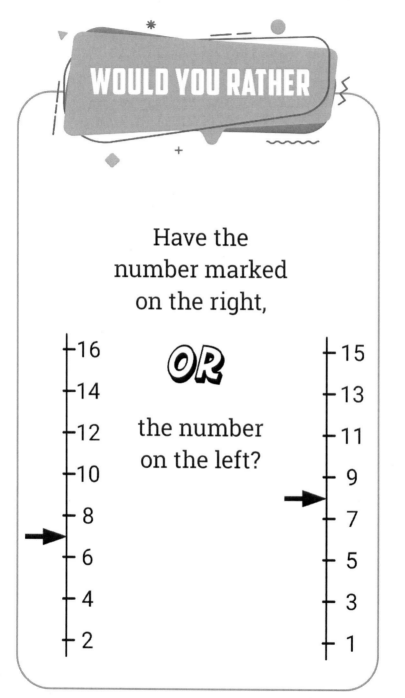

Have the
number marked
on the right,

OR

the number
on the left?

16   15
14   13
12   11
10   9
8   7
6   5
4   3
2   1

Have 'A',

OR

have 'B'?

A twelve subtract nine

B sixteen subtract six

☆ YOU LIKE BIG NUMBERS ☆

Say, "two more people walk rather than cycle to school,"

OR

"four more people walk rather than cycle"?

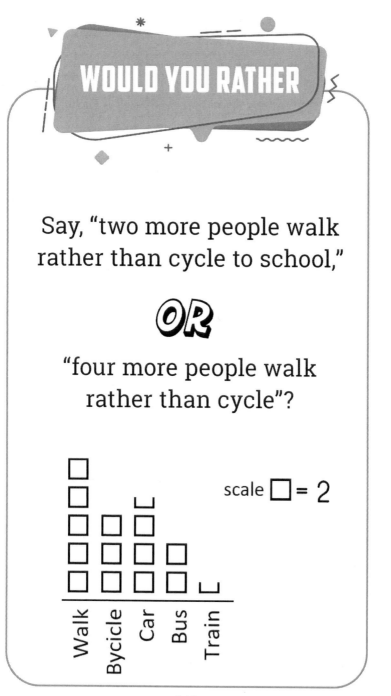

scale ☐ = 2

Walk | Bycicle | Car | Bus | Train

Prove that all the missing numbers are odd,

OR

that some of the missing numbers are odd, and some are even?

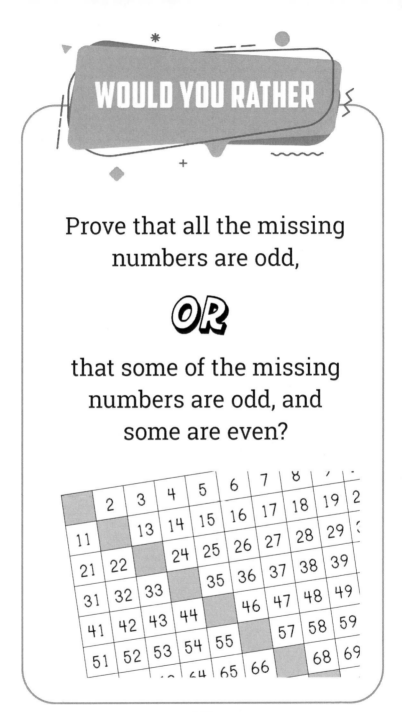

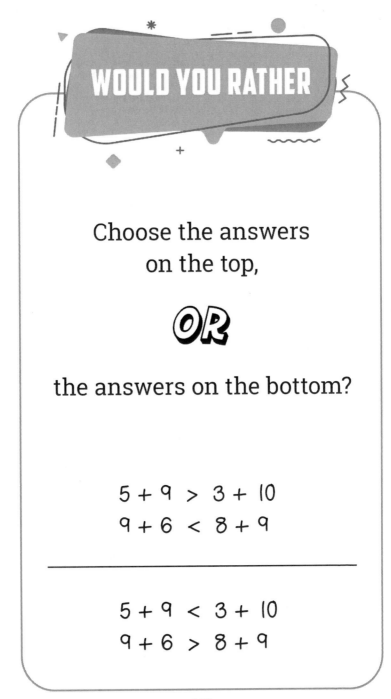

WOULD YOU RATHER

Choose the answers
on the top,

OR

the answers on the bottom?

$5 + 9 > 3 + 10$
$9 + 6 < 8 + 9$

$5 + 9 < 3 + 10$
$9 + 6 > 8 + 9$

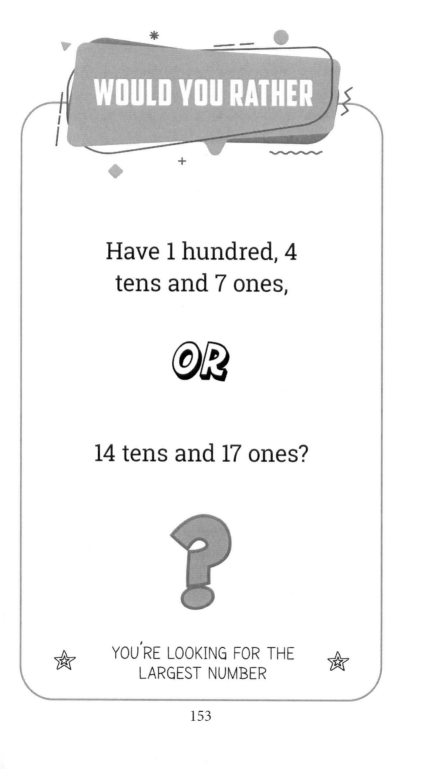

WOULD YOU RATHER

Have 1 hundred, 4 tens and 7 ones,

OR

14 tens and 17 ones?

YOU'RE LOOKING FOR THE LARGEST NUMBER

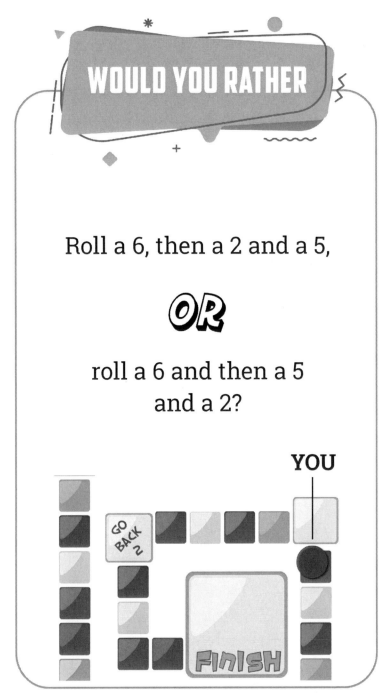

WOULD YOU RATHER

Roll a 6, then a 2 and a 5,

OR

roll a 6 and then a 5 and a 2?

YOU

GO BACK 2

FINISH

Show that half of 12 is the same as a third of 9,

OR

that a third of 12 is the same as half of 8?

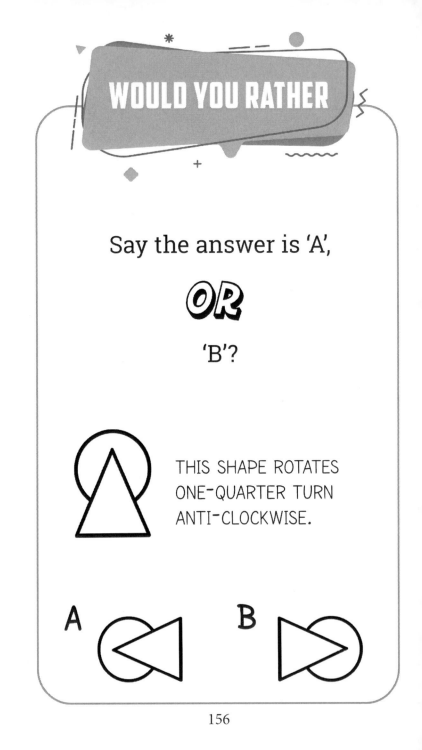

Say the answer is 'A',

OR

'B'?

THIS SHAPE ROTATES ONE-QUARTER TURN ANTI-CLOCKWISE.

A

B

Say, "two melons cost 50p,"

OR

"one melon costs 50p"?

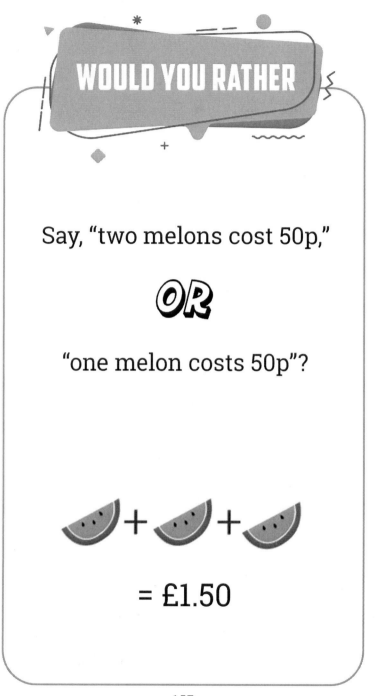

= £1.50

Use all these
shapes to make
a triangle,

 OR

use all these
shapes to make
a pentagon?

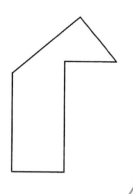

Have the sum of the numbers on the top line,

OR

the sum of the numbers on bottom line?

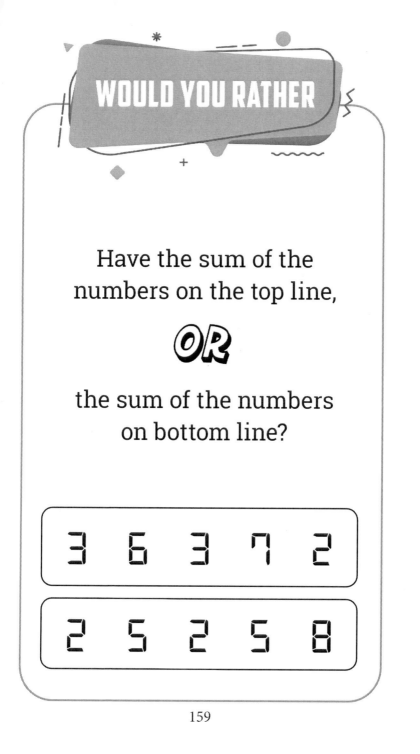

3 6 3 7 2

2 5 2 5 8

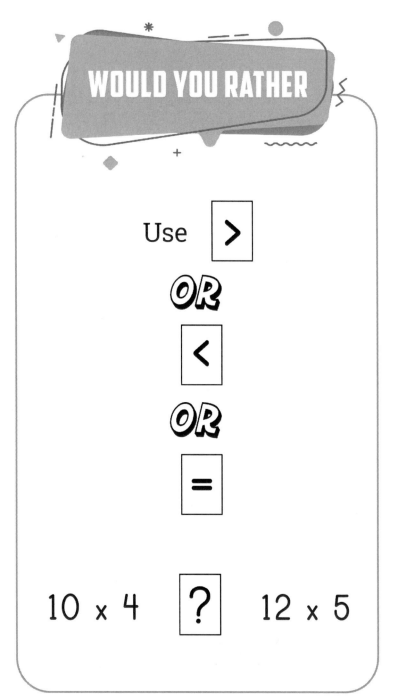

WOULD YOU RATHER

Use $>$

OR

$<$

OR

$=$

10×4 ? 12×5

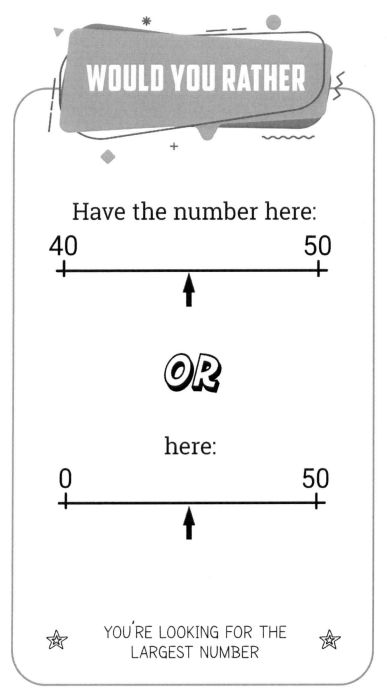

Have the number here:

40   50

OR

here:

0   50

YOU'RE LOOKING FOR THE
LARGEST NUMBER

WOULD YOU RATHER

Have the sum of the numbers on the right

OR

the sum of the numbers on the left?

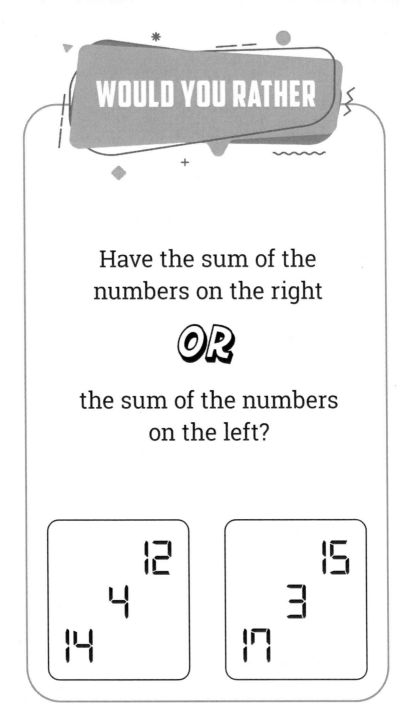

Go ice-skating every Saturday in December,

OR

every Sunday?

☆ YOU LOVE ICE-SKATING ☆

DECEMBER

S	M	T	W	T	F	S
1	2	3	4	5	6	7
8	9	10	11	12	13	14
15	16	17	18	19	20	21
22	23	24	25	26	27	28
29	30	31				

Thank you for downloading and reading this book, you're a superstar!

I hope you enjoyed making, and talking about all the mathematical choices. If you've found this book useful please leave a review. Even a few words would help others to decide if the book is right for them.

Thank you again - and remember...

"MATHS IS FOR EVERYONE AND EVERYTHING YOU DO COUNTS!"

John

mathsticks.com

Also from Mathsticks:

A Mathematical Would You Rather...
Key Stage 2

A further set of 150 mathematical choices - this time, specifically designed for older children.

Available on Amazon as an eBook and Paperback